GREAT SPORTS HOAXES

george sullivan

SCHOLASTIC INC.
New York Toronto London Auckland Sydney Tokyo

ISBN 0-590-32181-1

12 11 10 9 8 7 6 5 4 3 2 1 12 3 4 5 6 7/8

Printed in the U. S. A. 06